Dirty Gertie MACKINTOSH

JN

DIRTY GERTIE MACKINTOSH

DICK KING-SMITH

ILLUSTRATED BY ROS ASQUITH

CORGI BOOKS

DIRTY GERTIE MACKINTOSH
A CORGI BOOK : 0 552 528005

First published in Great Britain by Doubleday,
a division of Transworld Publishers Ltd

PRINTING HISTORY
Doubleday edition published 1996
Corgi edition published 1997
Corgi edition reprinted 1997, 1998

Corgi Books are published by Transworld Publishers Ltd,
61–63 Uxbridge Road, Ealing, London W5 5SA,
in Australia by Transworld Publishers (Australia) Pty. Ltd,
15–25 Helles Avenue, Moorebank, NSW 2170,
and in New Zealand by Transworld Publishers (NZ) Ltd,
3 William Pickering Drive, Albany, Auckland.

Made and printed in Great Britain by
Cox & Wyman Ltd, Reading, Berkshire

CONTENTS

Dirty Gertie Mackintosh
Never had a proper wash.
'Wash your hands,' her mum would say
Six or seven times a day,
But she never would obey.

Gertie Mackintosh was bad,
For she would pretend she had.
'Washed your hands?' her mum would cry.
' 'Course I have,' she would reply.
But it always was a lie.

Gertie simply couldn't stand
Using soap on either hand
Or her face. As well as those,
Gertie never blew her nose,
Never cleaned between her toes,

Never winkled out the wax
From her ears, nor washed their backs.
She would take a bath if told,
Lying there as good as gold
Till the water got too cold,

And she'd splash about and sing,
But she never washed a thing,
Not her body, nor her hair
Which was dark, though really fair.
She was dirty everywhere.

Soon, you possibly might think,
Gertie would begin to stink.
You'd be right. Before too long
Gertie gave out such a strong
And a penetrating pong

That it started to annoy
Every other girl and boy.
'Ugh! The smelly little fool!'
Cried the children at her school.
'Chuck her in the swimming pool!'

So, with a tremendous splosh,
In went Gertie Mackintosh.
As they watched her disappear
Underneath the waters clear,
Everybody gave a cheer.

'Swim!' they said. 'I can't!' she cried
To the children on the side
As she splashed about in vain.
Down she went and down again.
She was drowning, it was plain.

Someone watching gave a shout.
'Gertie! If we pull you out,
Will you promise you will be
Just as nice and clean as we
Are, for all eternity?'

'Yes!' gasped Gertie. 'Gurgle! Glug!'
So they gave her hair a tug,
Fished her from the waters green.
Never more was Gertie seen
To be otherwise than clean.

Miss Emily Berry was terribly strong.
Her legs were like tree trunks, her arms very long
And muscular, covered in gingery hair.
And Emily Berry could hug like a bear.

Not one of the boys, when it came to a fight,
Could possibly stand against Emily's might.
'Oh, stop!' each would plead as he struggled for breath,
With Emily squeezing him almost to death.

The fat ones, the skinny ones, tall ones or short,
Young Emily walloped whomever she fought.
Till one of them sneaked on Miss Berry at length
And told the Headmaster of Emily's strength.

'A girl in my school!' cried the Head. 'And she beats
The pants off each one of the boys that she meets?
I'll teach her a lesson, just wait and you'll see.
Send Emily Berry to come and see me.'

'Now Emily, what's this I hear?' asked the Head.
'You think you're the strongest of all, it is said.
You may beat up boys but I doubt if you can
Do much when it comes to a scrap with a man!'

So saying, the Headmaster took off his coat,
And slackened the tie that he wore round his throat,
And rolled up his sleeves, crying, 'Now, you young fool,
We'll see who's the champion fighter in school!'

Alas for the Head! In a trice he was trapped.
In Emily's arms he was tightly enwrapped.
How vainly he struggled, how wildly did gasp
As Emily Berry contracted her grasp.

Until, in that bear hug implacably held,
The last of his faltering breath was expelled.
And Emily Berry, I'm sorry to say,
Was also expelled on that very same day.

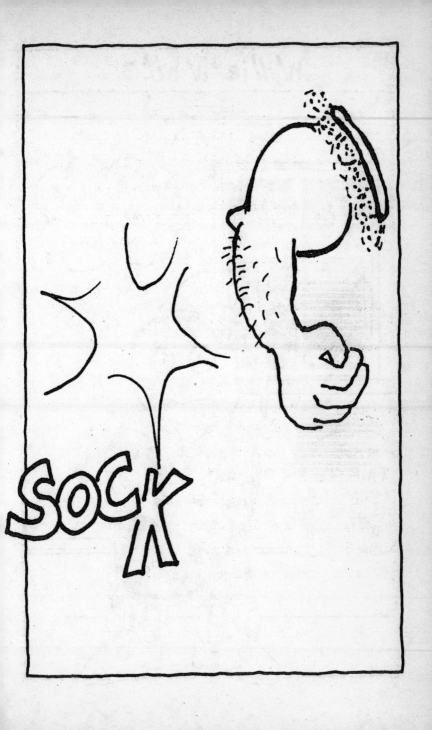

A little boy called Willie White
Would never go to sleep at night.
'I'm frightened of the dark,' he said
Each evening when he went to bed,
'So leave the light on if you will
And do not turn it off until
The nasty night has gone away.'
Then Willie White would sleep all day
Until at last they brought a plate
Of breakfast. This was served at eight
P.M. He had his lunch at one
A.M. His supper was begun
At dawn. And then, once it was light,
Straight off to sleep went Willie White.
Then came the day when Willie had
To go to school. The little lad
Was weary as could be because
He hadn't slept. No sooner was
He in his seat on that first morn
Than Willie White began to yawn,
And next he lay upon the floor
And very soon began to snore.

'What's up?' his teacher then enquired
Of Mrs White. 'Our Willie's tired,'
She said. 'The reason's plain, I think –
Last night he never slept a wink.'
Thereafter it became the rule
As soon as Willie got to school
He'd fall into an instant sleep.
So heavy was it and so deep
That it was useless, that was plain,
To try to wake him up again.
The other children learned to read
And do the things that children need,
Like sums, and learning how to write
And draw and paint, which Willie White
Could not be taught to understand
Because he was in slumberland.
And so he never learned a jot
But ended up a perfect clot
Who couldn't read or write or do
A simple sum like two plus two.

I do not think that you can fail
To see the moral of this tale.
Don't be like silly Willie White,
But always go to sleep AT NIGHT.

When Mrs Moon first saw her newborn son
Called Fred, she burst out into floods of tears.
'What's up,' asked Mr Moon, 'my honey-bun?'
Said Mrs Moon, 'His ears! Oh, look, his ears!'

So Mr Moon looked carefully at Fred,
And then, 'Cor, lumme, luvaduck!' he cried
In great surprise to see the baby's head
And what were stuck upon it, either side.

'I've never seen such ears in all my life!'
Said Mr Moon. 'They're twice as big as mine.'
'Oh, isn't it a pity,' said his wife.
'The rest of him is perfectly divine.'

The doctor said, 'We'll have to wait and see.
His ears may get no bigger. Who can tell?'
It was not so. When Fred had grown to three,
His ears had grown the same amount as well.

And when he got to four, the little chap
Amazed his parents even more. One day,
To their astonishment, they saw him flap
His giant ears to drive a fly away.

When Fred grew older and went off to school,
He wasn't very good at games or sport
And though he wasn't bright, in fact a fool,
Yet he was brilliant, everybody thought.

'His ears! Oh, look, his ears!' the children cheered.
'See how Fred Moon can wag them to and fro!'
His fame was such that shortly he appeared
On *Wogan* and *The Esther Rantzen Show*.

Thenceforward almost every single kid
In England, and a lot of grown-ups too,
Tried hard to twitch their ears the way he did,
But it was something only Fred could do.
(I've tried to do it and I can't. Can you?)

Lady Gwendoline Trench-Mortar
Was the one and only daughter
Of an Earl. With such a pater
She was educated, later,
At a girls' expensive college,
Where they filled her full of knowledge
Of the workings and appliance
Of the theory of Science,
French and German, Art and Woodwork,
In which Lady Gwen did good work,
Not to mention Greek and Latin,
And some other subjects that in
Time she proved that she could master.
No-one could have learned them faster.
Lady Gwen was not a shirker
But a dedicated worker,
And her permanent ambition
Was to be in first position.
Every time the girls were tested
Lady Gwen was never bested,
And she won so many prizes
That her head swelled several sizes
While she said things such as, 'Never,
Never was a girl so clever!'
Till at last nobody thought a

Lot of Gwendoline Trench-Mortar.
'Why, the boastful little creature!'
Said the other girls. 'We'll teach her
Not to be so darned conceited!'
And the punishment they meted
Out on Lady Gwen was: sending
Her to Coventry.

                    The ending
Of this story's rather zany.
Lady Gwen, although so brainy,
Did not know that to be sent to
Coventry just simply meant to
Say that nobody was talking
To you. So she set off walking
To the local railway station,
Coventry her destination.
Since she thought that Midland city
To be really rather pretty,
She remained there, not returning
To her recent place of learning.

Though both Earl and college sought her,
Lady Gwendoline Trench-Mortar
Then, despite their best endeavour,
Stayed in Coventry for ever.

Robert Jobbins, known as Bobby,
Had the most unusual hobby.
What, you ask, did he collect?
Not, I say, what you'd expect.
No, it wasn't stamps or suchlike.
Bobby's hobby wasn't much like
Any of the usual sort
That perhaps you might have thought.
'How we wish he had another
Hobby,' said his dad and mother
While they watched, with sighs and groans,
As their son collected . . . stones.
Stones of every size and fashion
Were his all-consuming passion.
Not a stone could Bobby pass,
By the roadside, in the grass.
Every single time he found one –
Big or little, square or round one,
Grey or brown or black or white,
Heavy rubble, pebble light –
Bobby took it home to add it
To the other stones he had. It
All provided endless joy
For the Jobbins' little boy.

Soon the fruits of Bobby's labours
Were apparent to the neighbours
As above the Jobbins' wall
There arose a heap so tall
Of these stones and rocks and boulders,
First as high as Bobby's shoulders,
Then, as the collection grew,
Blocking out the neighbours' view,
Rearing up towards the sky, a
Mountain rising ever higher.
Still did little Bobby roam,
Still he brought his prizes home,
Still in vertical direction
Rose and rose his stone collection.
'How much higher, d'you suppose?'
Said his father. 'Heaven knows,'
Said his mother. 'It's a pity,
For our garden once was pretty –
Roses, lupins, hollyhocks –
Now it's just a pile of rocks,
Nothing else but stones is in it
And it's growing by the minute.'
Grow it did till one fine day,
I am sad to have to say –
While the family were gazing

Upwards at that most amazing
Hill of stones of which you've heard –
That an avalanche occurred.
First there was a warning rumble,
Then the stones began to tumble.
None of them was left alive.
Not a Jobbins could survive.
Mum and Dad and little Bobby
Buried under Bobby's hobby.

Wendy Watson-Wilberforce
Doted on tomato sauce.
Everything she ate would fetch up
Liberally dosed with ketchup.
Not alone with fish or meat
But with anything to eat,
Wendy liked it covered in a
Sea of sauce. At breakfast, dinner,
And at tea-time it was strewed
Over all of Wendy's food.
Not a thing escaped the blessing
Of that red tomato dressing –
Sauce on Cornflakes or on Rice
Krispies tasted very nice,
Sauce on doughnuts, sauce on coffee-
Cake and sauce on treacle-toffee.
Wendy loved to eat the stuff
And at first this was enough,
Till, however wrong you think it,
She at last began to drink it.
Wendy soon, I'm grieved to say,
Drank two bottles every day
(Three on Sundays), which so shocked her
Mother that she called the doctor.
'Goodness me!' the doctor said.

'Wendy's face is rather red.'
Could it be, he thought, her heart? Oh,
She's the shade of a tomato!
First he listened to her chest,
Next he took some blood to test,
Then he drove away, full-throttle.
Wendy downed another bottle.
When the doctor came next day
This is what he had to say.
'What we found on analysing
Wendy's blood is quite surprising –
Not to worry you of course,
Mrs Watson-Wilberforce,
She's as healthy as a horse –
But . . . it's pure tomato sauce!'

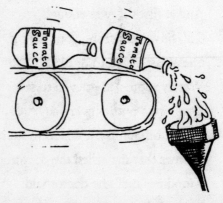

Clad only in a napkin made of flannel,

John Andrew Jones set out to swim the Channel.

The sea was rough, the water rather cold,

John Andrew Jones was not yet two years old.

His parents travelled in a boat beside him.

'He's wet,' said Mum. She wished she could have dried him

But Dad said, 'No, he's doing very well.

See how he breasts the mighty ocean's swell.

Watch how his little arms come up and over.

Already he's gone half a mile from Dover.

If he can keep it up, there's every chance

Tomorrow he will reach the coast of France.'

John Andrew Jones swam on as night was falling,

Undaunted, though occasionally calling

For baby-food or drinks of lemonade.

He did not seem in any way dismayed

Except that when the coming day was dawning –

His father dozing and his mother yawning –

He cried out, 'Mum! I want to have a wee.'

Said Mrs Jones, 'Well, do it in the sea!'

And so he did, which left him feeling happy,

And then, re-pinning carefully his nappy,

He swam until his father cried, 'Ahoy!

There's land not far ahead, John Andrew boy!'

Then, though the seas were turbulent and tossing,
John Andrew Jones achieved the Channel crossing,
And as his parents proudly clapped their hands,
He toddled stoutly up the foreign sands.
Oh, what a welcome was the lad accorded!
Oh, how the crowds of Frenchmen all applauded!
How loudly were John Andrew's praises sung!
'What swimming stroke was used by one so young?'
They asked. 'The breast-stroke? Or the doggy-paddle?'
And Mrs Jones replied, 'John Andrew's dad'll
Soon tell you.' 'There's no mystery at all,'
Said Mr Jones. 'John Andrew learned to crawl.'

A little girl named Esmeralda Bunn
Loved nothing better than to run and run.
Where others were content to walk, she raced.
What Esmeralda liked to make was haste.
Far speedier than any child alive
Was Esmeralda by the age of five.
Long-legged girls, big boys with knobbly knees –
She overtook each one of them with ease.
One Sports Day at her school this tiny tot
Went in for every race and won the lot.
Her father said, 'If only she were old
Enough to run, she'd likely win a Gold
At the Olympics.' Said her mother, 'Why
Not let our Esmeralda have a try?'
And so the Bunns all journeyed to Korea,
Where the Olympic Games were held that year,
To run her in the shorter of the sprints.
At first it wasn't easy to convince
The Games selectors that they ought to pick
The child. 'You wait, she's pretty quick,'
Said Mr Bunn. 'You'll be surprised, you know.'
So in a heat they let her have a go
(The Women's Hundred Metres), and the crowd
All burst out into laughter long and loud

To see her in her little vest and shorts
Competing in this speediest of sports.
Bang! went the gun, and off the runners went,
To win their sole ambition and intent,
But all the crowd had eyes for only one
And that of course was Esmeralda Bunn.
Her stumpy legs moved with such lightning speed
That very quickly she was in the lead,
And everybody watching was agape
To see her passing, first, beneath the tape
Which she of course was much to short to break.
'She won that fair and square and no mistake,'
Said Mr Bunn. 'She's easily the best.'
Said Mrs Bunn, 'Now she can win the rest.'
She did, right to the semi-final stage,
A feat unheard of at her tender age.
So now a Russian girl, a Swede, a Dane,
One from America, and one from Spain,
A tall Australian, a chunky Finn,
And Esmeralda waited to begin
The Final. As the starter raised his gun,
All eyes were fixed on Esmeralda Bunn.
How could she possibly expect to beat
This bunch of strapping girls, the world's élite?

Now as the runners settled in their blocks,
A light breeze stirring Esmeralda's locks,
The seven adult sprinters tense and grim,
Each nerve a-quiver, taut each muscled limb,
All those who watched could see the little child
Was quite relaxed. She actually smiled
While she was waiting on the starting line
As though to say, 'Just watch. This race is mine.'
Bang! And away she went at such a pace
That no-one else was really in the race.
Along the track the other runners tore,
But Esmeralda's heels were all they saw.
Unchallenged, past the winning post she flew,
She broke their hearts and broke the record too.
With pride her parents practically burst
To see that Esmeralda Bunn was first!
Now up the Duke of Edinburgh did come
And lifted her upon the podium,
And hung the medal round her little neck,
And shook her hand, and said to her, 'By heck!
Now "Bunn" will head the list of greatest names
The world has heard at the Olympic Games.'
And there the story ends. You've now been told
How Esmeralda ran to win the Gold.

Sitting beside his father and his mother,
His sister and his little baby brother,
Adolphus Brown was in an aeroplane.
Returning from a holiday in Spain.
The family were all relaxed and happy
And Mrs Brown had just changed baby's nappy,
When suddenly they got a nasty thrill.
The pilot of the plane was taken ill!
The crew then reassured them in a hurry,
'Co-pilot's in control – no need to worry.'
But then he too was taken ill as well,
And all the passengers began to yell.
'Keep calm!' came the command in tones emphatic.
The aeroplane flew on on automatic.
Then someone said, as through the skies they soared,
'Maybe there is a passenger on board
Who in the nick of time might be persuaded
To try to land the aeroplane unaided.
Someone perhaps who's qualified to fly.'
'Is there?' they asked. 'Yes!' cried Adolphus. 'I!'
'Adolphus!' said his mother. 'Don't be silly.'
'He'll never know the way to do it, will he?'
She asked her husband. He replied, 'He might.
Last week I showed him how to fly a kite.

He'd better try or we shall be the losers,
For beggars, after all, cannot be choosers.'
'Go on then, lad!' cried passengers and crew.
'The lives of all of us depend on you!'
'OK. Will someone show me to the right deck?'
Adolphus said. They took him to the flight deck
And sat him down before the instruments,
And watched him as with scrutiny intense
He scanned the great array of dials and meters.
Adolphus sat then in the pilot's seat as
The crew stood round him with their fingers crossed.
One false move from the boy and they were lost.
Had he the necessary understanding?
'Right,' said Adolphus. 'Where should we be landing?'
'Heathrow,' they said, 'or anywhere you please.
Gatwick. Or Stansted. Any one of these.'
Said Mrs Brown, 'Would Manchester be better?
That's where we live.' And so Adolphus set a
Straight course for Manchester, whose aerodrome
Was quite conveniently near his home.
He seemed to know exactly which was which as
He pulled the levers and he pressed the switches.
Onward they flew as steady as could be
Until Adolphus glimpsed the Irish Sea.
'Now then,' he said, 'we've got to find the Mersey.'

And so, dressed in his little shorts and jersey
He turned the aircraft round until he saw
The outlines of the Liverpudlian shore.
On, on they flew till Manchester was sighted.
'Well done, my boy,' said Mr Brown, delighted.
And now the little pilot was intent
On making an impeccable descent.
His flaps were down, his engine speed decreasing.
He watched the landing strip with care unceasing,
Until with expert ease Adolphus Brown
Eventually touched the aircraft down.
Oh, how relieved the passengers and crew were!
And when they cried, 'You were a hero, you were!
If it was not for you, we'd all be dead!'
'Don't mention it,' was all Adolphus said.

Mary Finn

A naughty girl named Mary Finn
Committed such a dreadful sin.
She went and put a drawing-pin,
Point upwards, on her teacher's chair.
The teacher came in, unaware
That Mary Finn had put it there.
But luckily she spotted it
In time, and so she did not sit
But walked around the room a bit
And looked at each and every child –
Most sensible, some meek and mild,
One insubordinate and wild.
Back to her desk the teacher went
And carefully, as though she meant
To sit upon the chair, she bent
Her knees. Of all the children in
The class, she saw one wore a grin.
It's her, she thought, it's Mary Finn.
She straightened up again. 'Oh dear,'
She said. 'My spectacles aren't here.
I left them in the Hall, I fear,
Just now when I was passing through.
So run and fetch them, Mary, do.
I know I can depend on you.'

Off Mary went on flying feet,
Determined not to miss the treat
Of seeing teacher take her seat.
She searched the Hall, but couldn't find
The spectacles. 'I must be blind,'
The teacher said. 'They're here, behind
This pile of books as plain as plain.
Now Mary Finn, sit down again.'
Then Mary gave a yell of pain
As something very sharp went in.
'Somebody's put a drawing-pin
Upon my chair!' cried Mary Finn.

A little boy called Obadiah Bird
Had quite the loudest voice you ever heard.
As soon as he was born, he gave a shout
So thunderous it blew the windows out.
'Did you hear that?' his startled mother said.
'Why, it was loud enough to rouse the dead!
He's got a pair of lungs and no mistake.'
'Oh!' said his father. 'How my head does ache!'
Alas, as little Obadiah grew,
His voice, can you believe, got bigger too.
Not only did it make his parents ill,
So penetrating was it and so shrill,
But all the neighbours started to complain.
'That voice,' they said, 'is driving us insane.
Whenever Obadiah makes a noise
It frightens all our little girls and boys
To hear that absolutely dreadful din.
We practically live on aspirin.
If Obadiah's yelling doesn't cease,
We shall report you Birds to the police.'
And so it wasn't very long before
A constable came knocking at the door.
'Mr and Mrs Bird?' he said. 'I'm told
That you've a little boy, not very old,

Whose noisy voice disturbs the neighbourhood.
I'd rather like to see him, if I could.'
To see him, thought the Birds, will be all right.
To hear him's going to give you quite a fright.
It did. When Obadiah said, 'HELLO!'
It horrified the poor policeman so
That hastily, before the boy could say
Another word, he turned and ran away.
The wretched Birds looked sadly at their son.
'Now see,' they said, 'what you have gone and done,'
As, near to breaking-point and close to tears,
They stuffed more cotton wool inside their ears.
The time went by. Things went from bad to worse,
As all who heard its horrid tones would curse
That voice. The Birds had constantly to move
In hopes that somewhere else things might improve.
So North they went, and South, and East, and West,
But everywhere they built another nest
The Birds would find that life was just as bad –
That awful voice drove everybody mad.
'The time has come,' said Mr Bird, 'I fear,
For us to live where nobody can hear,
Where there's no other house for many a mile.
At sea perhaps, upon a lonely isle

A reasonable distance from the coast.'
By great good fortune he secured a post
As lighthouse-keeper in the Irish Sea,
And there resided with his family.
He and his wife took turns to work the light
To warn the shipping in the dead of night,
And as for Obadiah, why, at last
There was a use for that tremendous blast
Of ghastly noise that issued from his throat.
It saved the anxious crew of many a boat.
In mist or murk, above Atlantic gales,
It reached the shores of Ireland as of Wales.
No louder foghorn was there ever heard
Than that produced by Obadiah Bird.

A pair of twins called June and Jane MacNee
Were as identical as twins can be.
Apart from differing in Christian name
Each sister was in every way the same.
Even their mother never really knew
For certain which was which or who was who,
And used to stand and gaze into the cot
Of one or other tiny little tot
And say, 'Now this is June. Or is it Jane?
Oh dear, I've got them muddled up again.'
But as from babes they changed to little girls,
Each with the selfsame mop of golden curls,
Another change took place with either twin,
For June grew tubbier while Jane grew thin,
Which meant that everybody very soon
Could easily distinguish Jane from June.
As time went on June ate and ate and ate
Till she was almost twice her sister's weight.
To stuff herself with food was her delight,
But Jane had very little appetite.
'Oh, what a worry!' said the twins' mama.
'What shall we do?' she queried their papa.
'We'd better get the doctor,' he replied,
'And quick, before the pair of them have died,

One from starvation, one from gluttony,
A quite unprecedented tragedy.'
The doctor came to see the ill-matched pair,
Each with blue eyes and each with golden hair,
But one of them abominably fat,
The other one as skinny as a rat.
The anxious parents hastened to explain
Which one of them was June and which was Jane.
'What shall we do?' they said. The doctor thought
Intently. Then he offered this retort.
'The only way,' he said, 'to put a stop
To things is this. You'll have to do a swap.
Exchange their names. You'll find that this will faze
The twins, and they will start to change their ways.'
And so they did, and Jane (now June) got plump,
While June (now Jane), no longer such a lump,
Lost weight. Until they weighed the same again,
Jane (also known as June) and June (ex-Jane).
And thus they stayed, and everybody saw
They were in shape identical once more.
In mind though they were never quite the same,
Each twin uncertain of her proper name.
'I'm June (or am I Jane?),' the one would sigh.
'I don't know who I am,' was the reply.

At last they asked their parents, the MacNees,
To call one 'Isobel' and one 'Louise'.
But June and Jane could never really tell
Who was Louise and who was Isobel.

A daring boy called Arthur Best
Set off to climb Mount Everest.
He did not tell his ma and pa
But thumbed a lift by motor car
To India. Then, for a change,
Walked to the Himalayan range.
To Everest itself he went
In readiness for his ascent.
Young Arthur, you can see, was bold,
Though rather less than ten years old,
And had no knowledge of the fears
That haunt experienced mountaineers.
But nonetheless he was not rash –
He'd taken seven pounds in cash,
Some Marmite sandwiches, a bar
Of chocolate, a biggish jar
Of peanut butter, and some pop
To drink when he had reached the top.
He had his father's walking stick
And wore a jumper that was thick
Because, so Arthur had been told,
On Everest it can be cold.
And one thing I forgot to say –

He took with him a large tin tray.
His preparations all complete,
His Doctor Martens on his feet,
Without a further waste of time
Young Arthur Best began to climb.
The lower slopes were simple stuff,
But then the way became more tough
Until the boy, for greater ease,
Got down upon his hands and knees
Which made him, amongst other thoughts,
Regret that he was wearing shorts.
The summit seemed as yet afar,
The route near perpendicular,
Yet undeterred was Arthur Best.
He stopped and had a little rest,
Unpacked his lunch and ate his fill,
Then pressed on upwards with a will.
By now his legs were feeling weak
But suddenly he saw the peak
And scrambled up the final crest
And stood triumphant. Arthur Best
Had reached the mighty mountain's top,
And so he drank his soda-pop.

Then, sitting on the large tin tray,
Arthur tobogganed all the way
Down Everest in much less time
Than it had taken him to climb.
And after that the little lad
Went home to see his mum and dad.
'Why, Arthur! Where've you been?' they cried.
'Up Everest,' the boy replied.
His parents didn't think this true.
How silly, for I'm sure you do.

Rupert Boot, an active boy,
Was his mother's pride and joy
As a babe. However, later
He began to irritate her
And his father also, thanks
To his many naughty pranks.
Rupert spent his pocket money
In the Joke Shop, buying funny
Imitation rubber flies,
Stink bombs and exploding pies,
Lifelike plastic doggy-messes,
And he'd drop down ladies' dresses
Hairy spiders. What delight
Rupert felt to see their fright.
With what laughter would he bellow,
Nasty-natured little fellow,
Every time he played a joke
On some unsuspecting folk.
Such as putting treacle-toffee
In his granny's cup of coffee,
And the shoe-polish he spread
On his grampa's slice of bread.
Granny cried, 'Oh, this is nasty!'
Grampa shouted, 'Damn and blast!' He
Spat it out upon the floor.

Oh, how Rupert Boot did roar!
In his auntie's apple custard
He put several squirts of mustard,
And some liquid soap, I fear,
In his uncle's glass of beer,
And was doubled up with laughter
At what happened to them after.
Till the day when Rupert went
To a pet shop. There he spent
All his money on a rather
Largish python. Wait till Father
Suddenly sees this, he thought.
Won't it be a bit of sport!
He'll be scared and so will Mother
And my sister and my brother.
All the family will get
Such a shock to see my pet.
Ah, but can you guess what followed,
Who it was the python swallowed?
Yes, you're right, the hungry brute
Made a meal of Rupert Boot.
Now the family were saddened.
Though the little boy had maddened
All of them, they couldn't take
Seeing him inside a snake.

'Cut it open,' one suggested,
And when this advice was tested,
Out popped Rupert, right as rain,
Back among the Boots again.
After that, so goes the rumour,
Rupert lost his sense of humour.
You may think that rather sad,
But the Boots were jolly glad.